FOLENS

IDEAS BANK

RE

SPECIAL PLACES

Louis Fidge
John Williams

Contents

Folens
Publishers

How to use this book

Ideas Bank books provide ready to use, practical, photocopiable activity pages for children, **plus** a wealth of ideas for extension and development.

TEACHER IDEAS PAGE   PHOTOCOPIABLE ACTIVITY PAGE

Clear focus to the activity.

Ways into the subject and background information for the activity.

Children's activity clearly outlined.

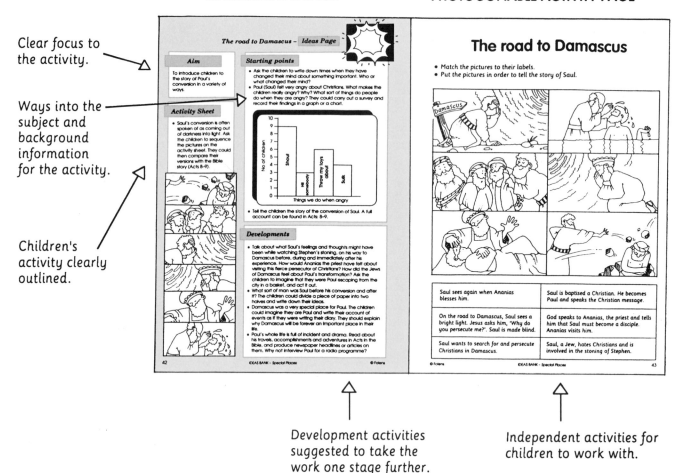

Development activities suggested to take the work one stage further.

Independent activities for children to work with.

- Time-saving, relevant and practical, **Ideas Bank** books ensure that you will always have work ready to hand.

The authors would like to thank Ivor Howes for his invaluable assistance in researching this book.

Cover by: In Touch Creative Services Ltd.   Illustrations by: Claire James   Cover photo: Zefa Pictures

Editor: Edward Rippeth.   Layout Artist: Suzanne Ward.

First published 1995 by Folens Limited, Albert House, Apex Business Centre, Boscombe Road, Dunstable, LU5 4RL, England.

ISBN 1852767472   Printed in Singapore

Introduction

A frequent claim made by educators is that the purpose of education is to educate the whole child, catering for the child's spiritual, moral, social, emotional, aesthetic and intellectual development. The reality in many primary schools, however, is somewhat different. Children's spiritual development is frequently given a low priority, according to recent research[1].

It is easy to understand why this might be. There are enormous burdens on the already hard-pressed teacher. As well as this, RE is a subject about which many feel uncertain, anxious or insecure. Research suggests that many feel they have insufficient personal knowledge[1], especially if they do not espouse any particular faith themselves. Another concern is that too little training is given and that there is a lack of good resources which are easily accessible and usable in the primary classroom. *Ideas Bank Special Places* is designed to help address this latter concern.

Over the last few years there have been many serious attempts to 'map out' more systematically what it is believed RE teaching in schools should involve. The view that has emerged is that RE teaching should include:
a) a 'knowledge' component relating to important facts, information and concepts.
b) an 'experience' component helping children to reflect on and respond to, their experiences so that knowledge can lead to understanding and insight.

Recent syllabus recommendations[2] have focused upon two key Attainment Targets:
● Learning About Religion
● Learning From Religion.

SCAA suggest that skills and processes should include investigation, interpretation, reflection, empathy, evaluation, analysis, synthesis, application and expression and that attitudes developed through RE should include commitment, fairness, respect, self-understanding and enquiry. *Special Places* sets out to incorporate these suggestions as far as possible.

In *Special Places*, children will develop their understanding through thinking about places which are special to them and the local and world community. They will learn about pilgrimages to special places and some important religious journeys. They will learn about world religions by focusing on faith community buildings. Wherever possible the resources should accompany visits to places of worship, reinforcing what they have learned about the way buildings, artefacts and symbols play a part in the worship, rituals and ceremonies. The *Special Places* resources will help fulfil the broadly accepted aim of religious education emphasised in the SCAA document: 'Pupils should be helped to acquire and develop knowledge and understanding of Christianity and other principal religions represented in Great Britain.'

Special Places resources provide accessible, flexible and immediate support for RE teaching. The units include essential background information, as well as ample opportunities for extending and developing the themes. Each unit may be treated as a single lesson, teachers taking from it only what is appropriate, although potentially each could be extended.

The resources include a wide range of stimulating and relevant photocopiable activities capable of being used across a wide age and ability range. The teaching notes generally include starting points for introducing main ideas and further ideas for extension and follow-up.

[1] REACH Religious Education and Collective Worship in Primary Schools, Culham College Institute, 1992

[2] SCAA Model Syllabuses for Religious Education, 1994

Aim

To encourage the children to see themselves as unique and their inner selves as special places.

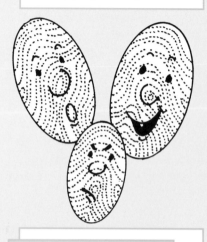

Starting points

- Talk about outward appearances and the way everyone looks different (facial features, clothes). No two people have the same fingerprints, everyone is unique.
- Ask the children to think of the different ways we categorise people. Then ask them to invent and label as many different characters as possible, using thumbprints (ink or paint) finished with detail. Make a collage of them and discuss their characteristics. How many of these characters do we meet in everyday life?
- Isaiah 49: 16 tells us that God knows us all individually and personally and has 'written your name on the palms of my hands.' Psalm 139 says 'For you (God) created my inmost being; you knit me together in my mother's womb. I praise you because I am fearfully and wonderfully made.' Discuss what these verses could mean.

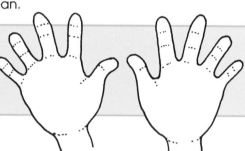

Activity Sheet

- Use the activity sheet in pairs to stimulate some thought on the question, 'Who am I?'
- Ask the children to make up more questions which have no real answer. If they could talk to the wisest person on earth, what sort of things would they ask him or her?

Developments

- Ask the children to draw their handprint and write their name inside it. Pass them around a group, and ask each child to write something they especially like about the handprint's owner. Then return the handprints to their owner, and ask if this is how they really are.
- Working in pairs (with a friend), ask the children to each think of, and write down, two things they would be able to tell a stranger, a neighbour, their parents and their good friends. Is there a difference in what they are prepared to tell different people?

What I can tell people	
A stranger	Nothing unless I'm with an older person
A neighbour	Mother's not well I'm doing well at school

- If possible, bring in some Russian dolls. Explain that we all have an exterior self which we show off to others. Ask the children how they behave in different situations – in school, to a policemen or with our friends. However, we also have a private inner self which may be very different. Ask the children to write down what they are like on the inside.

What would we be?

- Work with a partner. Each of you should answer the questions without talking about them.

If I were a colour, I would be
If you were a colour, you would be

If I were something to eat, I would be
If you were something to eat, you would be

If I were an animal, I would be
If you were an animal, you would be

If I were a drink, I would be
If you were a drink, you would be

If I were a musical instrument, I would be
If you were a musical instrument, you would be

If I were a flower, I would be
If you were a flower, you would be

If I were a building, I would be
If you were a building, you would be

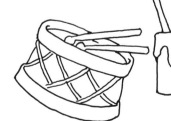

- Compare your answers. Talk about your reasons.

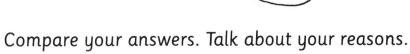

IDEAS BANK – *Special Places* 5

Aim

The aim of this unit is to encourage children to use their imaginations through fantasy. They might think about magical places, strange planets and the unknown, engendering a sense of mystery and awe.

My Space Fantasy
• Meet friendly aliens.
• Visit strange new worlds with lots of adventures.
• Eat strange food.

Activity Sheet

- After undertaking one or more of the above activities, ask the children to create a special place from their own imaginations, in poetry or through a drawing.
- Use the activity sheet. The children could paste their idea behind the door so that it remains hidden until someone opens the door and reveals it. Make a class book.

Starting points

- Read the opening part of the *The Lion, the Witch and the Wardrobe* by C S Lewis, where some children discover a doorway to the magical kingdom of Narnia in a wardrobe. Talk about the excitement of discovering unexplored places and imagining our own wonderful fantasies.
- Explain that you are going to take the children to an unexplored wood in their imagination. Create a suitable atmosphere by darkening the room and perhaps play some suitable pastoral music. Ask the children to sit comfortably and quietly, and talk them through the experience. Now invent the story.

  'The air is heavy and still. The sky is clear except for a few fluffy clouds. Birds are singing, bees buzzing...'

The Unexplored Wood

Developments

- Start exploring the theme of space by looking at pictures of planets, space craft, Earth seen from space. Play some suitable 'space' music if possible. Ask the children to discuss what they imagined and to produce a poem or a painting.
- Consider Psalm 8 which says: 'When I look at the sky which you have made, at the moon and the stars, which you set in their places – what is man, that you think of him; mere man that you care for him?'

> **What Heaven might be like**
>
> *Full of smiling, happy people.*
>
> *Very bright and colourful.*
>
> *Nobody does anything bad.*

- Ask the children to write down what they think Heaven might be like. The book of Revelation in the Bible paints a glorious picture of Heaven in various ways. It says that people will be with God for ever and there will be great rejoicing. There will be no night, for the glory of God will fill it with light. There will be no more death, crying or pain. God will wipe away every tear. Everyone will live in peace. Even the fiercest lion will be friends with the lamb.

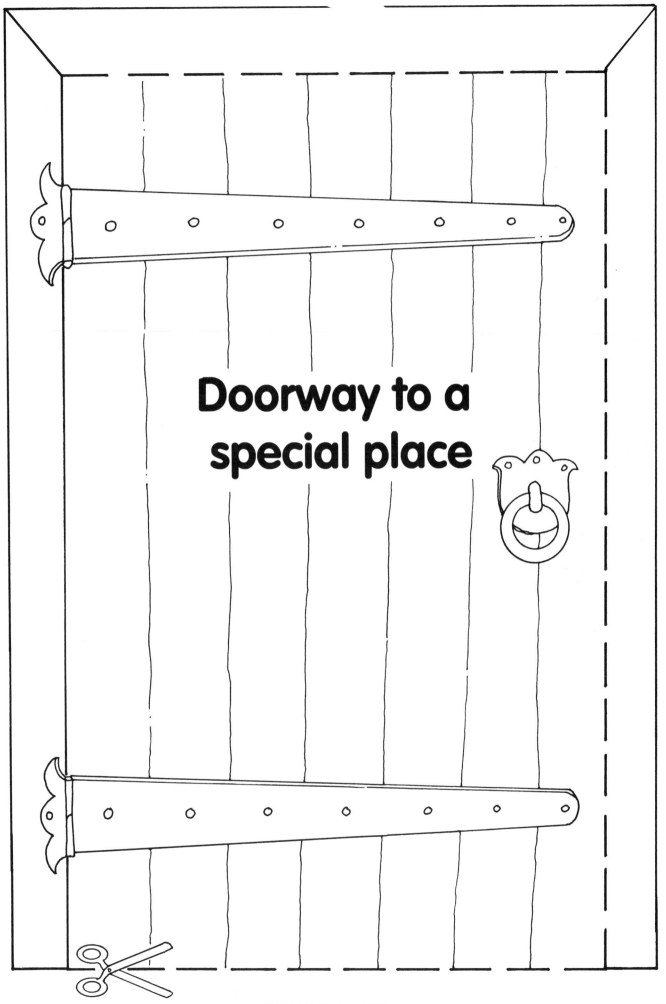

Doorway to a special place

IDEAS BANK – *Special Places*

Places of personal importance –

Aim

This unit considers places of very personal significance for the child, in the home or at friends or relatives. It asks children to consider what makes them special.

Top Secret STAY AWAY!

Starting points

- If possible read a little of Clive King's book, *Stig of the Dump*, and talk about the fact that the dump assumed enormous importance for Barney and Stig. It was their own special place, secret to them, where they could make their own world undisturbed by others.
- As a class, discuss places that are of special importance to different children. Ask where they are, and what is special about them. Are they places to be alone in or to share with others? Is there a difference?

My bedroom is a place to...
1. Read my books.
2. Play with my toys.
3. Think about tomorrow.
4. Listen to pop music.
5. Take my friends to.

Developments

- Bedrooms are often special places for children. What is it that they like about them? Do they ever escape there? From what or whom? What else do they do there? Make a list of at least ten things besides sleeping that children can do in their bedrooms. Set it out as a list poem and start each sentence with 'My bedroom is a place to...'
- Are there other rooms or places that have special significance, like the kitchen or garden? If so why?

My special place	Why it is special
My bedroom	I can be on my own
My friend's bedroom	We have lots of fun with his toys
My living room	Watch TV with family

Activity Sheet

- Ask the children to talk about stories of the 'Famous Five' type. Have the children ever formed a secret club or fellowship?
- Discuss any secret clubs they have been part of. Do they have a 'secret' meeting place? Are the members the same age?
- In small groups of four or five ask the children to brainstorm some ideas. Imagine they are forming a 'secret' club. Use the activity sheet for planning and collecting their ideas. Come together again as a class and share ideas.

- Discuss how we rarely have a chance to be alone with our thoughts. Is this important? Why? Read what one child wrote about bedtime: 'I love the time just before I go to sleep. I lie awake and go over all the events of the day and think about tomorrow. As I lie in bed I can hear familiar household noises, the TV, voices, the creaking stairs, someone coughing.' Where do children do their private thinking?

Our 'secret' club

• Write in the boxes and spaces the details of your secret club.

Club name

Password

Club members

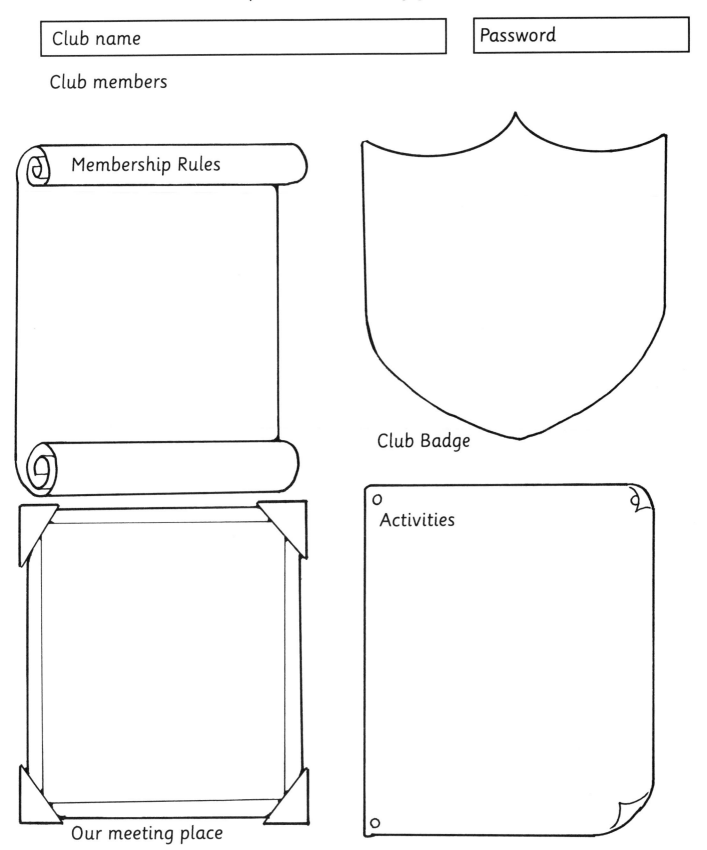

Membership Rules

Club Badge

Activities

Our meeting place

Places in my community –

Aim

To explore what community means by discussing the various groups children belong to. Encourage children to think about special places in their community and what is special about their community itself.

Starting points

- Talk about what groups the children belong to:

  Family: Who are the members of your immediate family? Do you know many other members of your family? What different duties and responsibilities are there within the family?

  School: What makes your school special? Are there any school rules? Is there a uniform? Why?

  Clubs: What clubs do you belong to? Why are they good?

  Faith communities: Do you belong to any religious groups who meet regularly or any clubs associated with them (Boys Brigade, Cubs etc)? Where do you meet? What sort of things do you do?

  Neighbourhood: What is your immediate neighbourhood like? Do any of your friends live nearby? Are people friendly? Do they help each other?

The following books help to develop an idea of community:

- *Babylon* by Jill Paton Walsh. A story about a West Indian community.
- *The Diddakoi* by Rumer Godden. Gypsy life is a strong theme in this book.
- *Gramp* by Joan Tate features the place of senior citizens in the community.

Activity Sheet

- If the children wanted to persuade someone to live in their community what would they say about it? Talk about the good points of living in their community. What things are not so good?
- Use the activity sheet to make a poster telling other people what a special place the children live in.
- The children could think of five reasons for coming to the place and write them on the sheet. They could draw a picture that they think captures the spirit of their community.
- Make a display of the posters.

Developments

- Brainstorm ideas about the places all communities need, for example, houses, shops (what sort?), places of worship. Ask the children to work in small groups and decide which are essential and which are not. Compare lists and discuss different viewpoints. Discuss the difference the size of the community makes: is it a village or town? Discuss the nature of the population: largely young/old, ethnic mix, mobile or static.
- Ask the children to each list five places or buildings in their community which are special to them. In pairs, explain to each other why they have chosen them.
- People like to send postcards from places they go to. Ask the children to think of something special about their community and design a postcard showing it in some way.

A very special place

- Design a poster to sell your community.
- What are the best points about it?
- How would you make the worst things sound better?

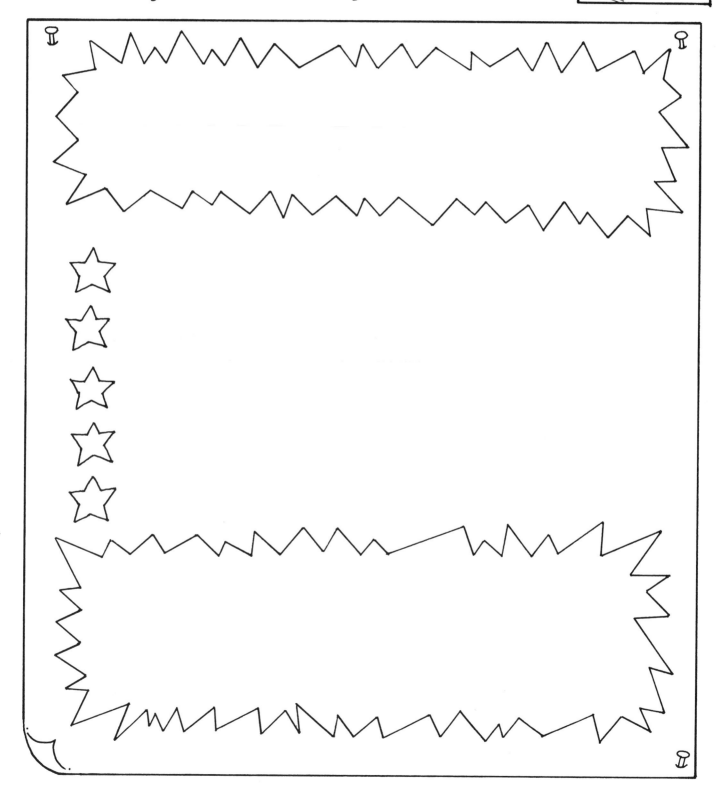

Construct a community – Ideas Page

Aim

To strengthen the children's understanding of community by playing a game in which they have to make their own community.

Living in my community
1. We don't drop litter.
2. We don't make lots of noise.
3. We help each other.
4. We talk to each other.

Starting points

- Remind the children that we all belong to different communities or groups, such as family, school, religious communities, locality. Belonging to a community involves having some responsibility towards it, the need to think of others and a degree of commitment.
- There are often rules that we have to follow. Talk about the local community in which they live. Discuss whether it is a good place to live. Are people friendly and helpful? Are there good facilities and services?

Rules for activity sheet

- Each group has to construct and agree on a community.
- They are allowed to move the items around on their paper as often as they wish until they reach complete agreement.
- Everyone in the group must be allowed to express their thoughts and ideas.
- All items from SET A must be used.
- Only 12 of the items from SET B may be chosen.
- More roads are allowed. Sort out the positioning of the items first and when satisfied add any other roads needed.

Activity Sheet

- Ask children (in groups or five or six) to construct a community according to certain rules. They should talk together and come to an agreement.
- Give out the activity sheets (one per group):
  - Cut up the sheets into two parts, Set A and Set B.
  - Stick set A on to one colour card, Set B on to another.
  - Cut up the separate items from each set.
  - Place the items from each set into separate envelopes (enough for one set of each items for each group).
  - Supply one sheet of A3 paper for each group (this should have two main roads drawn on it).

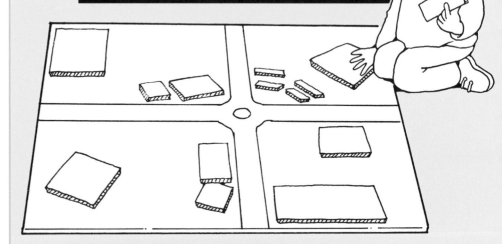

Developments

- The value of the activity is in the negotiation, consideration, evaluation and working together, using everyone's ideas. The teacher could move from group to group, making suggestions and resolving differences of opinion.
- When groups reach a satisfactory conclusion, ask them to stick their items permanently down on to the A3 paper. Display the finished results for purposes of comparison and discussion.

Construct a community

SET A

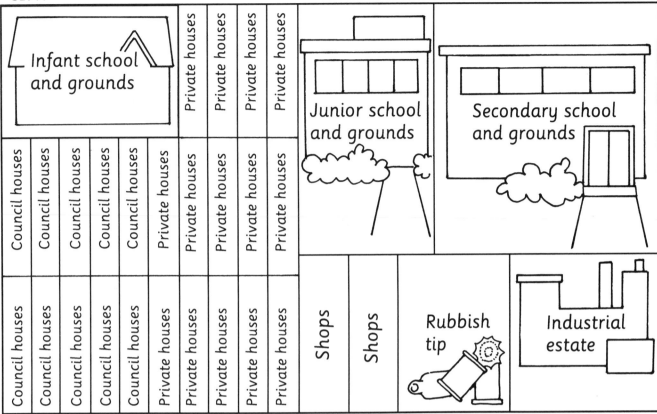

SET B

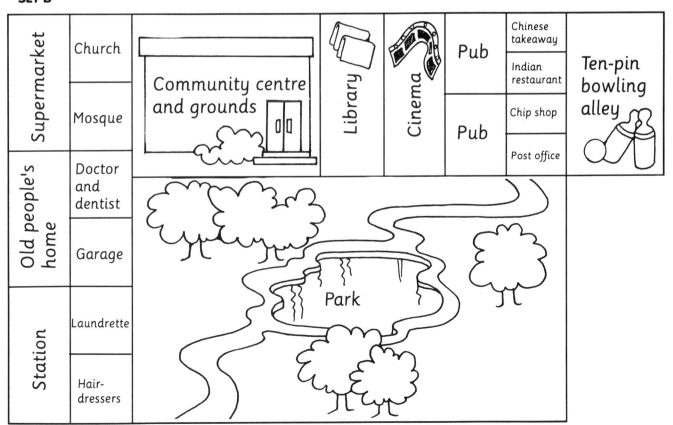

What's in a building? –

Aim

To consider the physical construction of places and their functions and how they are special to people.

Starting points

- What makes a house a home? What building materials are used in making a house? What people are needed? What turns a building into a home? Talk about personal possessions, people, memories and experiences.
- Ask the children to divide a piece of paper into two, with the heading 'A house' on one side and on 'A home' on the other. Brainstorm ideas and write 'ingredients' lists for both sides. The children could also make up a 'There's no place like home' poster or Victorian sampler.

Developments

- Ask the children to do a survey of the school, using a school plan if possible - or one the class has made.

A school survey

- How many classrooms does it have?
- What other rooms does it have?
- What other facilities does it have (car park, playground, fields)
- What materials is the school made from?
- What services (gas, electricity) does it need?
- What paid staff are needed to run it?
- Are there any voluntary workers who help the school?
- How old is it?

- If possible, look at the school's prospectus and consider how it 'sells' the school. Ask the children to list the things that could persuade parents to send their children there.
- Ask what makes school a special place. Is it the lessons, teachers, things you do, friends, playtimes, lunches or after-school activities? When they look back, what special memories will the children have of school? Ask them, with a partner, to compose a shared piece of writing on the theme.

Activity Sheet

- Ask the children to interview each other using the activity sheet survey.
- They should record their results on their sheet.
- Talk about the purpose of each place, the people who use them and why they may be special (for example, by giving pleasure, for worship).

IDEAS BANK – *Special Places*

A buildings survey

- Ask some of your classmates if they have visited any of these places and fill in the spaces.

	Names								
a supermarket									
a shopping mall									
a church									
a cathedral									
a cinema									
a theatre									
a mosque									
a library									
a concert hall									
a theme park									
a gurdwara									
a museum									
a leisure centre									
a synagogue									
a temple									
a castle									
a zoo									
a sportsground									
an ice-skating rink									

- When you have completed your survey, find out what makes two of these buildings special.

An Anglican church – Ideas Page

Aim

To consider the design and purpose of an Anglican church and why this is a special place for Christians.

Starting points

- Share with the children information about Anglican churches, or ask them to research Christian places of worship and what is found in them. Are all Christian churches similar?
- Children from church-going families could share their experiences of church life.
- A local minister could be invited to talk to the class.

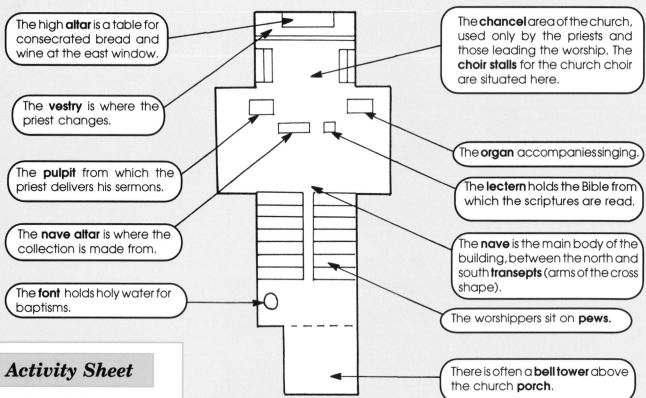

The high **altar** is a table for consecrated bread and wine at the east window.

The **vestry** is where the priest changes.

The **pulpit** from which the priest delivers his sermons.

The **nave altar** is where the collection is made from.

The **font** holds holy water for baptisms.

The **chancel** area of the church, used only by the priests and those leading the worship. The **choir stalls** for the church choir are situated here.

The **organ** accompanies singing.

The **lectern** holds the Bible from which the scriptures are read.

The **nave** is the main body of the building, between the north and south **transepts** (arms of the cross shape).

The worshippers sit on **pews.**

There is often a **bell tower** above the church **porch**.

Activity Sheet

- The activity sheet could be used to accompany a discussion, or a visit to a church building.
- Help the children to relate the plan to the diagram and label the diagram.

Church visit
a) What we saw.
b) What we touched
c) What we heard

Developments

- Plan a visit to a local church. Ask the children to consider:
- **The church interior**: name and identify parts of church, furniture and their functions, symbols used and so on.
  Using the senses:
  (a) Sight: parts of the church, the stained glass windows;
  (b) Touch: rubbings, different materials used;
  (c) Sound: organ, bells, echoes, singing, or silence;
  (d) Smell: flowers, polish, musty smell, candles;
  (e) Taste: bread/wafers, wine – and their symbolism.
- **History**:
  (a) Architecture: look at doors, windows, mouldings, columns, gargoyles. Compare drawings of different architectural styles: Romanesque (600-1200), Gothic (1200-1600), Renaissance/Classical (1600-1837), Victorian and later.
  (b) Other clues: look at graveyards and tombstones.
- Investigate the life and people of the church.

An Anglican church

- Work with a partner. Look at the plan of the church and then label the diagram.

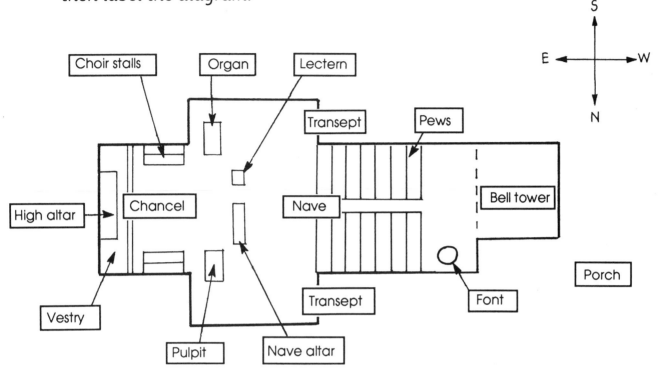

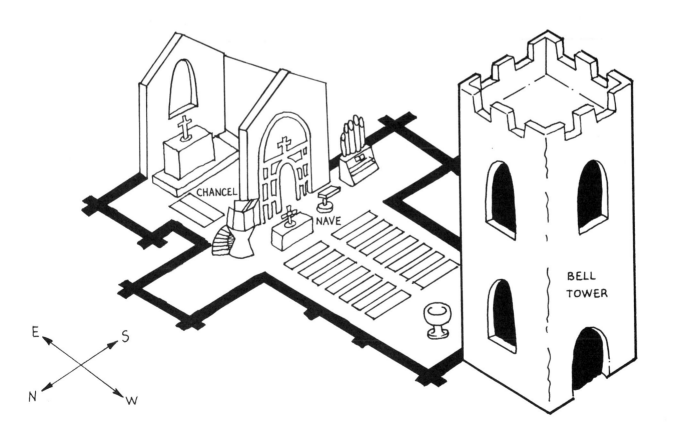

A Baptist church – Ideas Page

Aim

To learn about the design and purpose of a Baptist church and why this is a special place for the members of one Christian denomination.

Starting points

- Share with the children information about Baptist churches, or ask them to research Christian places of worship for various denominations and what is found in them.
- Children (and perhaps parents) of church-going families from non-conformist/Baptist/free church backgrounds could share their experiences of church life.
- Invite a local Baptist minister to talk about his/her training, beliefs, style of dress, role in the church etc.

The Anglican Church's break from Rome in 1534 triggered the development of other protestant, non-conformist and free churches, like the Baptists. They moved towards places of worship which were simpler and more practical, with no set design.

At the back of the church is a **room** where the ministers and elders dress and make ready the service.

There are **galleries** or **balconies** so lots of people can attend.

A **pulpit** where the minister preaches from.

The worshippers sit on **pews** which are usually wooden. They are arranged so that people can see everything and be fully involved in the service.

The **altar** is usually a plain wooden **table** for communion. The simple wooden crosses (rather than crucifixes) emphasise the belief that Jesus died on the cross and rose again.

The **baptistry** is a sunken pool with steps either side allowing total immersion for adult and 'believer's' baptisms.

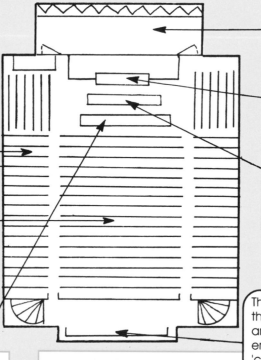

The **entrance** where elders greet the congregation as they arrive and leave the church, as Baptists emphasise the people are the 'church' not the building.

Activity Sheet

- The activity sheet could be used to accompany a discussion, or visit and follow-up to a church building.
- The children could answer the questions and compare their responses.

Developments

- The belief in 'believer's' and adult baptism is a very important part of the Baptist faith. Find examples of baptism in the Bible's New Testament (Luke 3: 1-20, Matthew 3: 13-17). Discuss the differences between infant and adult baptism. What symbolism is involved?
- If possible, plan a visit to a local Baptist church.
  The church exterior: Does it look like a 'church'?
  The church interior: What features are most noticeable? Identify the focal point for worship around which everything is arranged. Identify and name parts of the church, furniture and their functions, symbols used etc. Can the children find a Bible, hymn or prayer book?
  The life of the church: Find out who uses the church (general services, special occasions, private worship etc); what church organisations and groups there are; what links the church has with the community (youth work, missionary support).

A Baptist church

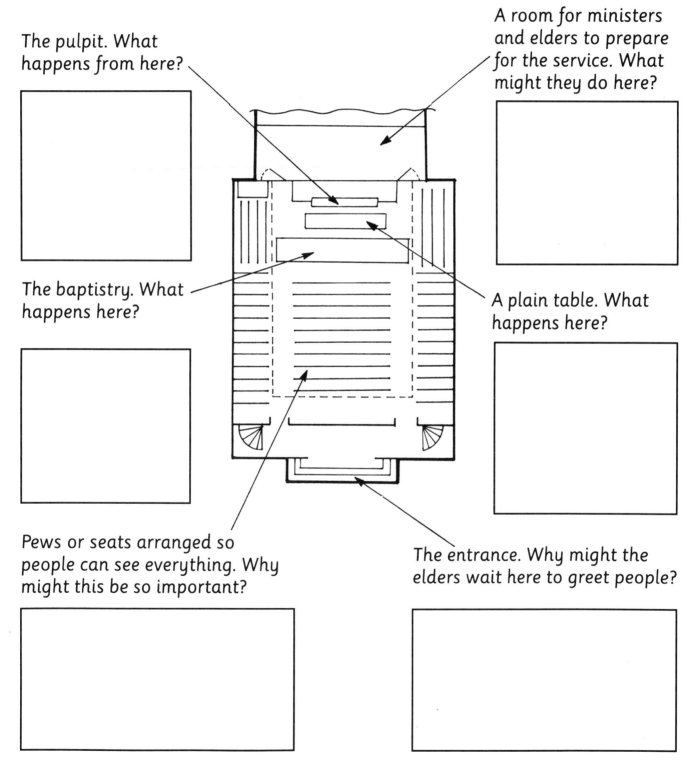

- Using the spaces provided, answer the questions about this layout of a Baptist church.

The pulpit. What happens from here?

A room for ministers and elders to prepare for the service. What might they do here?

The baptistry. What happens here?

A plain table. What happens here?

Pews or seats arranged so people can see everything. Why might this be so important?

The entrance. Why might the elders wait here to greet people?

NOW • Now compare your answers to your class-mates.

A cathedral – Ideas Page

Aim

To learn why cathedrals are important places to Christians and how their magnificent appearance reflects this.

Starting points

- Share with the children information about cathedrals, or ask them to research the features and location of them.
- Ask them to share their experiences of any visits to cathedrals, their impressions and memories. Ask them to discuss why they think people built cathedrals and and to imagine being a worker, erecting scaffolding, carving wooden pews, being a stone mason, often high above the ground. How are cathedrals different from smaller churches?

The word cathedral comes from the Latin 'cathedra' which means 'seat'. Hence a large church becomes a cathedral if it contains a bishop's 'seat', a throne from which he exercises his authority over his 'Diocese' (district). Cathedrals are important because:
- they are the mother churches for all the parishes in the diocese.
- they provide an ornate and dignified setting for worship.
- they are an expression of local pride, with the best design and craftsmanship.
- they often have great musical and historical traditions.

A feature common to most cathedrals is their sheer size and grandiose majesty. The scale and beauty of the exterior **indicate** that a cathedral took many years to build, and demonstrate the skilled dedication of the finest craftsmen, master builders, stone masons and carpenters of the time.

Cathedral visit
1. What noises and music is there?
2. What does wood and stone feel like? Do a rubbing.

Activity Sheet

- Stained glass windows were made to tell Bible stories visually to illiterate people.
- Using Bibles, children could find out what the stained glass window on the activity sheet might represent and talk about the meaning of the story.
- Use the sheet as a template to make more stained glass windows for display.

Developments

- Investigate the history of your nearest cathedral and people associated with it. What can the children discover about a newer cathedral like Coventry? Research the life of Christopher Wren and St Paul's Cathedral in London.
- If possible visit your nearest cathedral. Explore it:
  - **through the senses**: through its sounds and music (and its silence); through the touch and texture of wood and stone (do some rubbings); through its smells – the flowers, candles, incense; through taste (cathedral honey?); through sight, sketching and drawing selected things.
  - **through symbolism:** find examples and talk about the symbolism that is everywhere.
  - **through its external architecture**.
- Discuss what furniture can be found in cathedrals, its function and appearance. Find or draw pictures to make a display.

Stained glass windows

- Shade in this stained glass window to reveal the story.
- Use a Bible to find out which of these stories it tells.

Luke 2: 16	Mark 1: 22-24
Matthew 13: 18-23	John 12: 13-14

- Why was it important in the past to tell stories from the Bible using pictures?

The mosque – Ideas Page

Aim

To learn something of the design and purpose of a mosque and why this is a special place for Muslims.

Starting points

- Share with the children information about mosques, or ask them to research Muslim places of worship and what is found in them.
- Muslim children could share their experiences and impressions of the mosque.
- Invite the local imam to come into school and bring artefacts with him. Ask him about his training and his role.

Other rooms in a mosque are used for social and educational purposes.

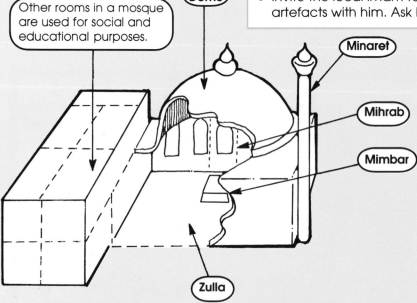

Dome
Minaret
Mihrab
Mimbar
Zulla

Muslims worship in a **mosque** (a place of prostration). Mosques are traditionally rectangular in shape, with walls separating the sacred area. Footwear should be removed before entering. The ablutions process, known as **wudu**, includes the methodical washing of hands, face and feet.

The inside of the mosque is deliberately sparse, reducing distraction and the fact that no intermediaries are required in worshipping Allah. The walls may be decorated with abstract patterns and stylised calligraphy texts, taken from the **Qur'an** in Arabic – no images of Allah, man, beast or plant are allowed. In some mosques there are also rooms for library and educational resources, meeting and community facilities.

Activity Sheet

- This sheet should be used to accompany a discussion on, or visit and follow-up to, a mosque.
- The children could use the labels to explain the diagram.

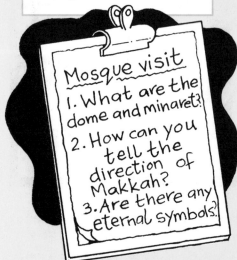

Mosque visit
1. What are the dome and minaret?
2. How can you tell the direction of Makkah?
3. Are there any eternal symbols?

Developments

- Plan a visit to a local mosque if possible. Focus on:
  The mosque exterior: discuss the shape and design of the minarets and dome. Are there any beautiful tiles or examples of Islamic patterns and calligraphy? How can you tell which direction Makkah is? Are there any external symbols used, like the crescent or half moon shape? What are their meanings?
  The mosque interior: is there a focal point around which everything seems to be arranged? Where is the Qur'an placed? What key features, furniture or symbols are apparent? What is their purpose or meaning? How are the various rooms used?
  Use of the mosque: how often is the mosque used? What is it used for? What special celebrations take place at the mosque? Find out about the educational uses of the mosque. Is it ever used for community as well as religious purposes?
- Prayer is at the heart of the Muslim faith. Discuss what prayer means and its significance to a believer. Find out about the Muslim washing procedure, Wudu. Is there a set sequence? What is its symbolic significance? Find out about the muslim prayer and genuflection procedure (the full sequence involves twelve prayer positions).

The mosque

- Read the information below and label A–E on the diagram.
- Use the diagram and information to explain the design and uses of a mosque.

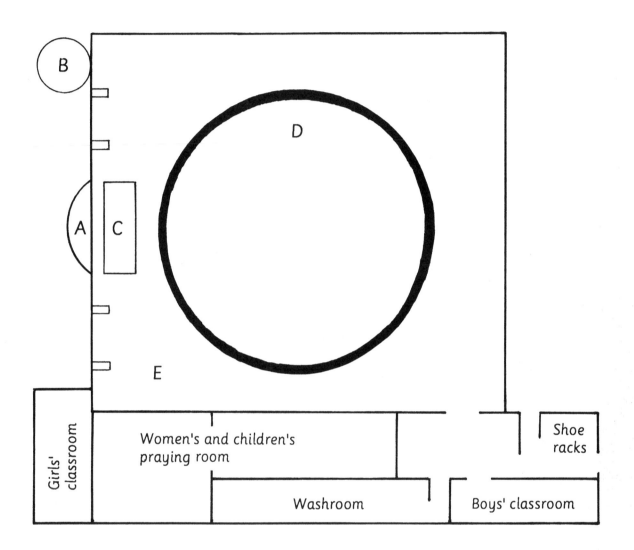

<table>
<tr><td>Mihrab
A small niche showing the direction of Makkah for prayer.</td><td>Minaret
Tower used to call Muslim to prayer five times a day.</td><td>Zulla
The main prayer room for men.</td></tr>
<tr><td>Washroom
For washing before worship: wudu.</td><td>Shoe racks
Shoes must be removed before entering the mosque as a mark of respect.</td><td>Women's and children's prayer room
A separate room where these people pray.</td></tr>
<tr><td>Mimbar
The pulpit from which the imam preaches.</td><td>The dome
This represents the Universe and the great love of Allah.</td><td>Classrooms
Where Muslim boys and girls come to learn Arabic so they can read the Qur'an.</td></tr>
</table>

The Buddhist Vihara – Ideas Page

Aim

To learn about the variety and location of Buddhist places of worship and why they are special for Buddhists.

Starting points

- Share with the children information about the Buddha and Buddhist places of worship, or ask the children to research these: their design, location and what is found in them.
- Ask any Buddhist children (and perhaps their parents) to share their experiences and impressions of attending the Vihara.

The Five Elements of the Vihara

Buddhist temples vary in design from country to country, but they are usually built to symbolise the five elements – wisdom, water, fire, air and earth. Whilst Buddhists do not have a fundamental belief in God, they do pay homage and give reverence to Buddha in their search for enlightenment.

Buddhists attend their temple, **Vihara**, as often as they can. In the **shrine room** there is a large image of the Buddha and statues of his disciples. Images and statues do not recreate a god or life form, but help the worshipper to focus more clearly on the subject of their meditation. The shrine always faces east because of the direction of the sunrise. A bell is often used to call the faithful to prayer. Shoes are removed before the entrance to the shrine. There are candles (symbolising light), flowers (a present to Buddha), incense (lit as a tribute to Buddha).

1. Wisdom
2. Water
3. Fire
4. Air
5. Earth

Vihara Visit
1. Exterior – shapes, design.
2. Interior.
3. Use.

Developments

- If it is possible plan a visit to a Vihara. Focus on:
  The exterior: talk about any obvious external features. Discuss the different shapes and designs of the Buddhist temples around the world.
  The interior: is there a focal point around which everything seems to be arranged? What key features, furniture or symbols are apparent? What is their purpose or meaning? Where can the Holy Scriptures be found? What can you discover about them? Are there other rooms besides the shrine room? How are they used?
  Use: how often is it used? What is it used for? What special celebrations take place there?
- The first Buddhist school in England opened in Brighton in 1994. How different might it be from the children's school? Produce a list of rules and a possible timetable.

Activity Sheet

- Talk about what the temples have in common. Introduce the idea that the design is based on the five elements.
- Ask the children to use the clues and the map to find the names of Buddhist temples in various countries and their location.

BUDDHIST SCHOOL TIMETABLE

DAY	MORNING		AFTERNOON	
MONDAY	ASSEMBLY HOMAGE TO BUDDHA	SCIENCE	MATHS	MEDITATION

Buddhist temples

- Look at the six Buddhist temples from different countries. Match the shapes and use the clues and the map to find out what they are called and where they are from.
- Complete the chart.

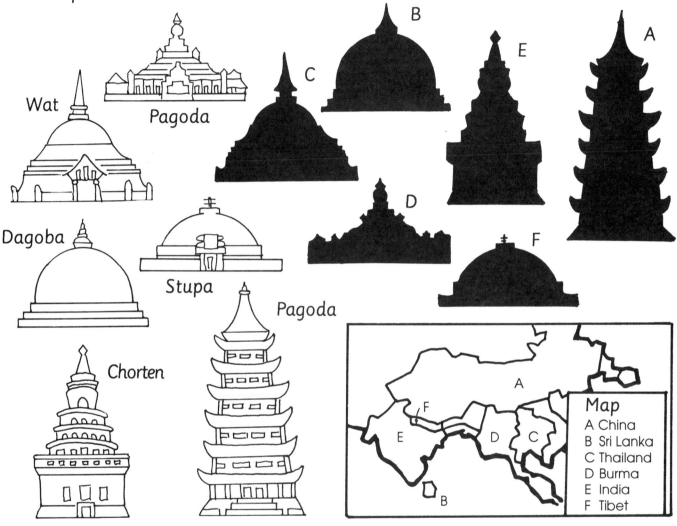

	Name of temple	Country where it can be found
A		
B		
C		
D		
E		
F		

A Hindu mandir – Ideas Page

Aim

To learn something of what is found in a Hindu mandir (temple) and why this is a special place for Hindus.

Hindu temples in this country tend to be converted buildings with offices, a community hall, a kitchen and accommodation for the priest as well as the main worship area.

In the **sanctuary** is a carpeted area and **shrines**. The shrines contain marble **statues**.

In the **central shrine** is usually Rama, Sita (his consort) and his brother Laksham. All the statues are washed daily by the priest.

Above the shrines is a canopy and the **sikhara** which represents the sacred mountains.

Starting points

- Share with the children information about the mandir, or ask the children to research Hindu places of worship.
- Ask for their ideas about what places of worship should look like. Do they have to be specially built? Could buildings be converted? Could a place of worship be anywhere?
- Hindu children, and perhaps their parents, could share their experiences and impressions of attending the mandir.

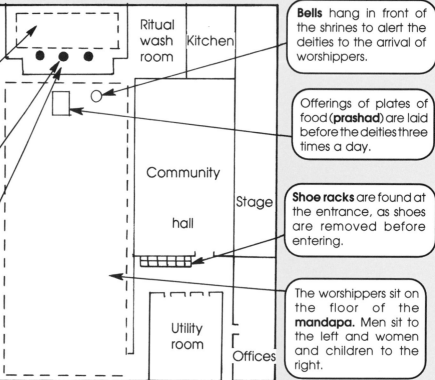

Bells hang in front of the shrines to alert the deities to the arrival of worshippers.

Offerings of plates of food (**prashad**) are laid before the deities three times a day.

Shoe racks are found at the entrance, as shoes are removed before entering.

The worshippers sit on the floor of the **mandapa.** Men sit to the left and women and children to the right.

Mandir visit
1. Is there a focal point.
2. What are the key features.

Activity Sheet

- Use the activity sheet to follow up a visit to a mandir. Ask the children to discuss the names of the key features of a Hindu mandir and place them on the the diagram.

Developments

- Ask the children:
  Is there a focal point around which everything seems to be arranged? What key features, furniture or symbols are apparent? What is their purpose or meaning? Where can the Holy Scriptures be found? What can you discover about them? Are there other rooms besides the main sanctuary? How are they used? How often is the mandir used? What is it used for? What special celebrations take place there? What sort of music is used in Hindu celebrations?
- Ask the children to research the following:
  - Arti, a welcoming ceremony.
  - Prashad, holy food offered to the gods.
  - Krishna and other Hindu gods.
  - the Hindu belief in reincarnation.
  - Puja, the Hindu form of worship.

A Hindu mandir

● Label the diagram using the information below.

| The bell to tell the deity that worshippers have arrived. |
| A shrine with statues of the deity. |
| The shaped roof (sikhara) above the shrine representing the sacred mountain. |

| The worship area (mandapa). |
| Shoes taken off and left at the door, before worship. |
| A Hindu worshipper. |

● The following are also found in a mandir:
    – offices   – utility rooms
    – community halls   – kitchen
● What does this tell you about the uses for a mandir other than worship?

The Sikh gurdwara – Ideas Page

Aim

To learn about a gurdwara and why this is a special place for Sikhs.

A gurdwara (literally 'doorway to the guru') is any room which contains a copy of the **Guru Granth Sahib**, the sikh holy scriptures. In Britain they are often converted houses, old churches or schools, and all fly a **flag** called the **Nishan Sahib**. Often the phrase 'Ik Onkar' will be seen outside the gurdwara, meaning 'there is only one God'.

Starting points

- Share with the children information about the gurdwara, or ask them to research Guru Nanak, Guru Gobind Singh, Baisakhi and Sikh worship.
- Ask for their ideas about what places of worship should look like. Do they have to be specially built? Could buildings be converted? Could a place of worship be anywhere?
- Sikh children, and perhaps their parents, could share their experiences and impressions of attending the gurdwara.

The **Guru Granth Sahib** is on a stool (**manji sahib**). When it is not being read it is covered by a silk cloth (**romalla**).

An ornate canopy (the **palki**) is set above the Guru Granth Sahib.

To the left of the scriptures is a bowl of sanctified food (**karah parshad**). All gifts of money and offerings of food or fruit are laid on the platform (**takht**).

The reading is often accompanied by **ragis** (musicians).

Shoes are removed before entering the gurdwara. Men and women cover their heads as a mark of respect. When they are worshipping, everyone sits on the carpeted floor, the men to the right and the women to the left.

Behind the holy scriptures sits a male or female reader (**granthi**). There are no formal priests in Sikhism. The reader may be holding a **chauri** (a fan of yak hair or nylon, which is waved over the Guru Granth Sahib).

Gurdwara visit
1. Find the focal point.

Activity Sheet

- This activity sheet could be used to accompany a visit to a gurdwara. The children could relate the plan to the diagram and label the picture accordingly.
- They should discuss the reasons for their choices.

Developments

- Try to visit a local gurdwara. Ask the children:
  Is there a focal point around which everything seems to be arranged? What key features, furniture or symbols are apparent? What is their purpose or meaning? Where can the Holy Scriptures be found? What are they called? What can you discover about them? Are there other rooms besides the main gurdwara? How are they used? How often is the gurdwara used? What is it used for? What special celebrations take place there? What sort of music is used in Sikh celebrations?
- **Research**: What more can be discovered about the following:
  – A Sikh marriage ceremony.
  – Baisakhi.
  – The Golden Temple of Amritsar.
  – Ardas, a Sikh service.
  – The Sikh ceremony of Amrit Parchar.

A Sikh gurdwara

● Work with a partner. Look at the plan of the gurdwara and then label the diagram.

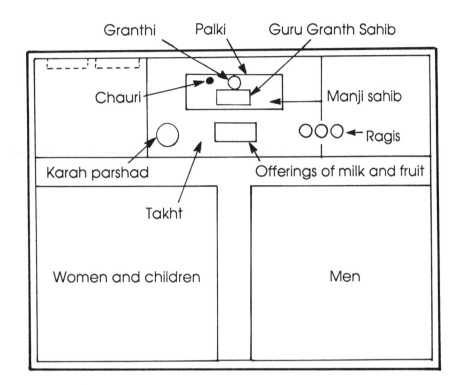

Granthi   Palki   Guru Granth Sahib

Chauri

Manji sahib

Ragis

Karah parshad   Offerings of milk and fruit

Takht

Women and children   Men

An Orthodox Jewish synagogue – Ideas Page

Aim

To learn about an Orthodox Jewish synagogue and why this is a special place for Jews.

Starting points

- Share with the children information about synagogues, or ask them to research Jewish places of worship and what is found in them. Jewish children could share their experiences of Bar and Bat Mitzvah and life at the synagogue.
- A local rabbi could be invited to answer questions.

Activity Sheet

- The activity sheet could accompany a discussion, or visit and follow-up to an Orthodox Jewish synagogue.

'Synagein' is the Greek word for 'to gather together'. The criteria for any synagogue to be an official place of worship was that ten Jewish males had to be present. In Orthodox synagogues, women and children sit in upstairs galleries, while in Liberal and Reform synagogues, everyone sits together. The building is generally rectangular and is usually built facing Jerusalem. Three sides of the building have seats facing inwards.

At the centre of the synagogue, in front of the **pulpit**, is a raised platform with railings (the **Bimah**). Here, the person conducting the service reads from the **Torah** and invites members of the congregation to do likewise.

Rooms adjacent to the synagogues are used for community meetings, Hebrew study classes and kindergartens.

The **Ten Commandments** are written on two plaques above the ark.

A traditional oil lamp, the **ner tamid,** is suspended above the ark (lamp of eternal light), and is named after the menorah light of the Jerusalem Temple.

Behind a curtain (**parochet**) on the fourth wall facing Jerusalem, is a cupboard (**ark**) where the Torah (the first five books of the Bible) is kept.

Community Centre

Hebrew classes

Uses for a synagogue

Promote Jewish culture.

House of law for domestic issues. eg. Kosher meat

Developments

- Visit a local synagogue. Ask children to name and identify some of it, the furniture and their functions and the symbols used. This could be followed up by creating a classroom synagogue for a day, in order to share their understanding with others.
- Model arks and parochets could be made, stained glass windows designed, inscriptions placed above them to denote their significance. Research Bible texts for these, for example, Joshua 24: 24, Deuteronomy 7: 12, 8: 11, Psalm 119: 1, Psalm 2: 105.

An Orthodox Jewish synagogue

- Look at the diagram of a synagogue.
- Research what happens in a synagogue and complete the chart.

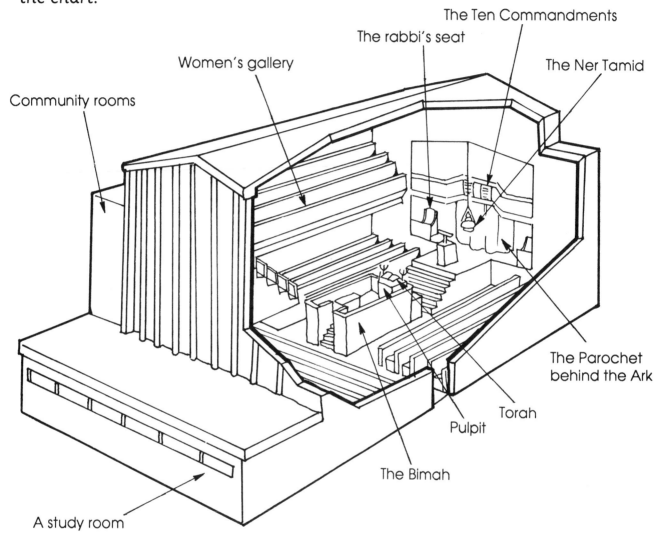

Feature	What it is
Bimah	
Ner Tamid	
Parochet	
Torah	
Pulpit	

Going places – Ideas Page

Aim

To consider the anticipation, excitement, planning and nature of the journey when going to a special place.

Starting points

- What school trips do the children remember best? What are their favourite places visited? They could carry out a survey of the class and display their findings as graphs and charts. Talk about their anecdotal experiences.
- What sort of places do children go to with their families on days out? What is special about family days out? What is the most special place visited? Why?

Activity Sheet

- Use the activity sheet as a quiz to see who can identify these well-known landmarks and places. Further points could be gained by adding where they are to be found.
- Follow up the quiz by discussing each one briefly and ask the children why they might be special places.

Quiz answers

1. Pyramids, Cairo, Egypt
2. St Paul's Cathedral, London
3. Statue of Liberty, New York, U.S.A
4. Eiffel Tower, Paris, France
5. Taj Mahal, Agra, India
6. Tower Bridge, London
7. Stone-henge, Salisbury Plain
8. Brandenberg Gate, Berlin, Germany
9. Sydney Opera House, Sydney, Australia
10. Statue of Christ, Rio de Janeiro, Brazil
11. Ayers Rock, central Australia
12. Wembley Stadium, London

Developments

- Distribute holiday brochures and ask the children to pick one place they would like to go to. Explain how holiday brochures use persuasive language to 'sell' the destinations. What would you say about your town or village to persuade people to visit it? Make a display of postcards of special places children have visited on holiday. Map out the stages of a holiday, including anticipation, planning, packing, the journey, settling in, the holiday and the aftermath.
- Is there a cemetery or crematorium near? Why do people visit cemeteries? Why are they special places? Why do people take flowers? Visit a local churchyard and conduct the time there with respectful quiet. Talk about why it is important to do so. What were the children's thoughts and feelings as they read the inscriptions on the graves?

Special places quiz

● Identify the places and find out where they are.

Place:
Location:

Place:
Location:

Place:
Location:

Place:
Location:

Place:
Location:

Place:
Location:

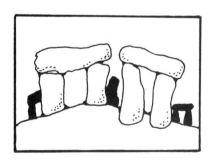

Place:
Location:

Place:
Location:

Place:
Location:

Place:
Location:

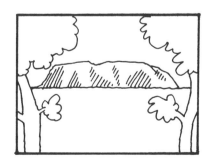

Place:
Location:

Place:
Location:

Pilgrimage: The Hajj -

Aim

To develop an understanding of the concept of pilgrimage and to look in detail at the Hajj.

Starting points

- Share with the children information about the stages in the Hajj, or ask them to research pilgrimage.
- Talk about and list the reasons for each of the actions and how Muslims might feel at each stage.

Pilgrimage

This is a practice common to the followers of many religions. Muslims have the Hajj; some Christians will journey to Walsingham, Lourdes, or St Peters in Rome; Jews to the Wailing Wall in Jerusalem; Hindus will try to bathe in the River Ganges; Sikhs to the Golden Temple at Amritsar; Buddhists to the temple at Bodh Gaya where the Buddha gained enlightenment. A pilgrimage involves both the journey and a spiritual quest for something.

The Hajj

One of the Five Pillars (rules) of Islam is that wherever possible a believer should visit Makkah, Saudi Arabia, where the Prophet Muhammad is buried. Hajj means 'to set out for a definite purpose' and is a way of showing obedience and worship to Allah (God). Before reaching Makkah, at Miqat, pilgrims must cleanse themselves and put on special white robes called 'ihram', which symbolise unity and equality. After following the stages on the activity sheet, the pilgrims return to the mosque at Makkah and circle the Ka'bah one last time.

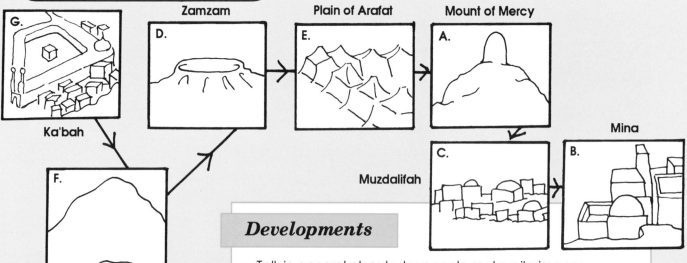

G. Ka'bah — Zamzam D. — Plain of Arafat E. — Mount of Mercy A. — Muzdalifah C. — Mina B. — F. Safa and Marwa

Developments

- Talk in general about why people make pilgrimages. Ask the children to find out more about pilgrimages carried out by other faiths. (See the list in the general background notes above.)
- **The boy Jesus at the Temple**. Read the story of this pilgrimage to a special place in Luke 2 and discuss its significance. Try telling the story from different people's points of view.

Some useful reading on pilgrimages:

Pilgrim's Progress by John Bunyan (a children's version).
I am David by Anne Holm which tells of a boy's escape from a concentration camp and his search for identity.
The Road to Canterbury by Ian Seraillier (a selection from Chaucer's Canterbury Tales).
The Small Miracle by Paul Gallico - a boy and a donkey's journey of faith in Assisi.
Watership Down by Richard Adams - a band of rabbits leave the safety of their burrow and venture into the unknown.

Activity Sheet

- Ask the children to complete the activity sheet. This involves choosing the correct captions for each part of the plan, reinforcing the sequence of events at Hajj.
- Research further the history of the Ka'bah and its importance to pilgrims.

The Hajj

● Label what happens on the Hajj. Find out why.

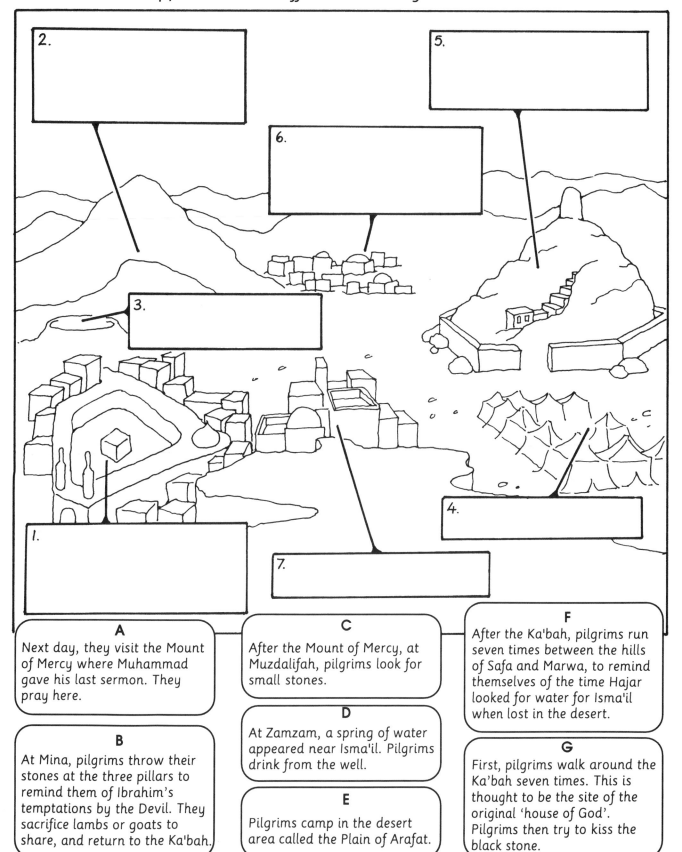

2.

5.

6.

3.

4.

1.

7.

A
Next day, they visit the Mount of Mercy where Muhammad gave his last sermon. They pray here.

B
At Mina, pilgrims throw their stones at the three pillars to remind them of Ibrahim's temptations by the Devil. They sacrifice lambs or goats to share, and return to the Ka'bah.

C
After the Mount of Mercy, at Muzdalifah, pilgrims look for small stones.

D
At Zamzam, a spring of water appeared near Isma'il. Pilgrims drink from the well.

E
Pilgrims camp in the desert area called the Plain of Arafat.

F
After the Ka'bah, pilgrims run seven times between the hills of Safa and Marwa, to remind themselves of the time Hajar looked for water for Isma'il when lost in the desert.

G
First, pilgrims walk around the Ka'bah seven times. This is thought to be the site of the original 'house of God'. Pilgrims then try to kiss the black stone.

Jerusalem – Ideas Page

Aim

To learn about the importance of Jerusalem to people and particularly pilgrims of many faiths.

Starting points

- Share with the children information about the history of Jerusalem, or ask them to research what is important in the city to Christians, Muslims and Jews.
- Investigate what the children understand by a journey. Consider the idea of a pilgrimage and why people go on these journeys.

Jerusalem

- **1000 BCE** The Jewish capital under King David and a resting place for the Ark of the Covenant (a religious centre for the twelve tribes of Israel).
- **961-922 BCE** Solomon builds a temple on Mount Zion.
- **597-587 BCE** The temple is desecrated by Babylonians and the Jews are exiled.
- **165 BCE** The temple is re-dedicated by Herod.
- **70 CE** Romans violate Jerusalem and desecrate the temple.
- **335 CE** Emperor Constantine builds a church on site of the Holy Sepulchre (where Jesus was buried).
- **637 CE** The city falls to Arab invaders.
- **1099 CE** Christian Crusaders take control.
- **1517** Muslims recover Jerusalem.
- **1917** British take over sovereignty.
- **1948** Palestine is partitioned and Jerusalem is declared a UN area.
- **1950** Jerusalem is declared the capital of Israel.

'BCE' means 'before Common Era' which started with the birth of Jesus. 'CE' is the Common Era.

Developments

- Christians often travel the Via Dolorosa (the Way of the Cross) at Easter, retracing the last steps of Jesus before his crucifixion. Significant events of Jesus' progress to the cross are marked at 14 places – the 'Stations of the Cross'. Tell the children the Easter story or ask them to find the 'stations' in the Gospels.
- John Bunyan wrote 'Pilgrim's Progress' while in jail because of his beliefs. He saw the journey through life as a difficult pilgrimage, where God influenced the way he thought, acted and behaved. Read sections from an abridged version of the book and discuss the words of his famous hymn:

  'He who would valour see, let him come hither
  One here will constant be, come wind come weather;
  There's no discouragement, shall make him once relent,
  His first avowed intent – to be a pilgrim.'

  William Blake's 'Jerusalem' could also be read or sung.

Activity Sheet

- For many people, a pilgrimage is not just a journey, but involves the heart and the mind.
- The journey may be the experience of a lifetime, with many challenges and hardships, but ultimately worthwhile.
- Play the 'pilgrimage' game on the activity sheet. The children will need counters and a dice.

Pilgrim's progress

● Be a pilgrim. Play the game to reach Jerusalem.

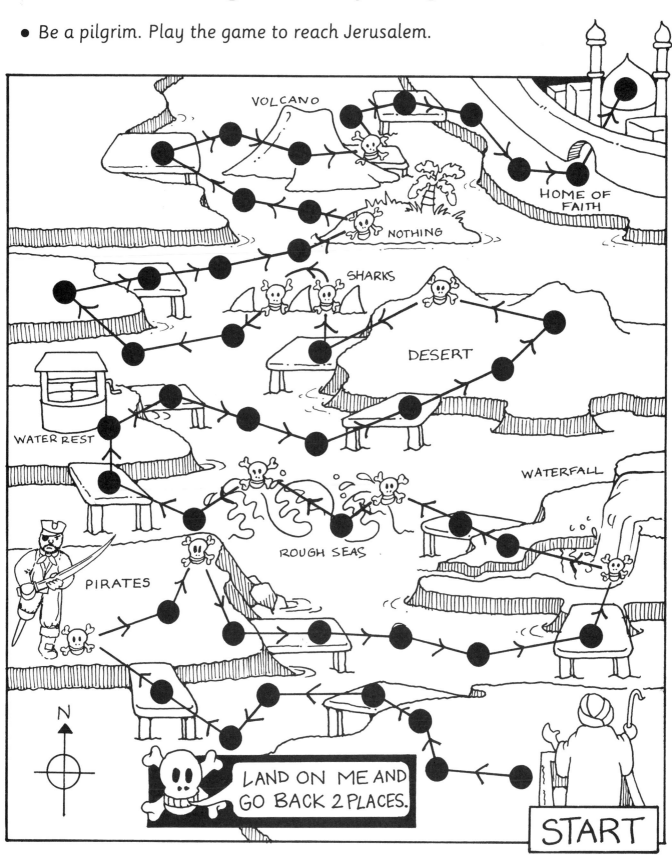

The Vatican City – Ideas Page

Aim

To learn something of the importance of the Vatican and why it is a special place for Roman Catholics.

Starting points

- Share with the children information about the Vatican, or ask them to research this.
- Locate Rome on a map. Research something of its history and influence during the peak of the Roman Empire. When did Christianity arrive there?
- Ask the children what they know of St Peter, his work in spreading the Church and his martyrdom?

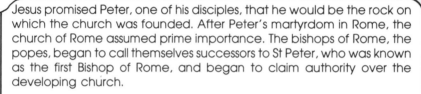

Jesus promised Peter, one of his disciples, that he would be the rock on which the church was founded. After Peter's martyrdom in Rome, the church of Rome assumed prime importance. The bishops of Rome, the popes, began to call themselves successors to St Peter, who was known as the first Bishop of Rome, and began to claim authority over the developing church.

Rome, the centre of the church's growth, provided a territorial home for the Pope. The Vatican City was established in 1929 as an independent state within the city of Rome. It is one square kilometre in size and has about 800 inhabitants. It is the headquarters of the Roman Catholic church, administered by a governor appointed by the Pope.

The Vatican has its own flag, postal service, telephone and radio system and daily newspaper. It mints its own coins and has law courts, libraries, museums, a road and rail network, gardens and places of learning. One of the most famous of the Vatican's buildings is St Peter's Basilica.

Activity Sheet

- By discussing and prioritising the clues on the activity sheet, the children could find out why the Vatican is a special place, particularly for Roman Catholics.

The Pope
1. Lives in the Vatican City.
2. Is elected by Cardinals.
3. Stays Pope until he dies.

Developments

- Peter was reputedly crucified in Rome at a time when Romans saw Christianity as a threat to their power. Discuss the struggles the early church had in establishing itself against repression and persecution. Are there places in the world today that still have little religious freedom? Why?
- Peter means 'rock'. He was the foundation on which Christianity was established. Research and discuss the meanings of children's names. Who chose them? Was there any special reason? Do they capture different children's personalities?

My name	Its meaning	Reasons
Edward	Prosperous guardian	Grandad's name
Alison	Noble	It sounds nice
Peter	Rock	After Peter Finch
Raymond	Light of the world	Dad liked it
Noel	Christmas	Born at Christmas

- Find out what children know about the Pope. Write some facts given by the children on the board. Ask them to find out more about the Pope.

The Vatican

• Look at the clues. Decide what makes the Vatican a special place and complete the chart.

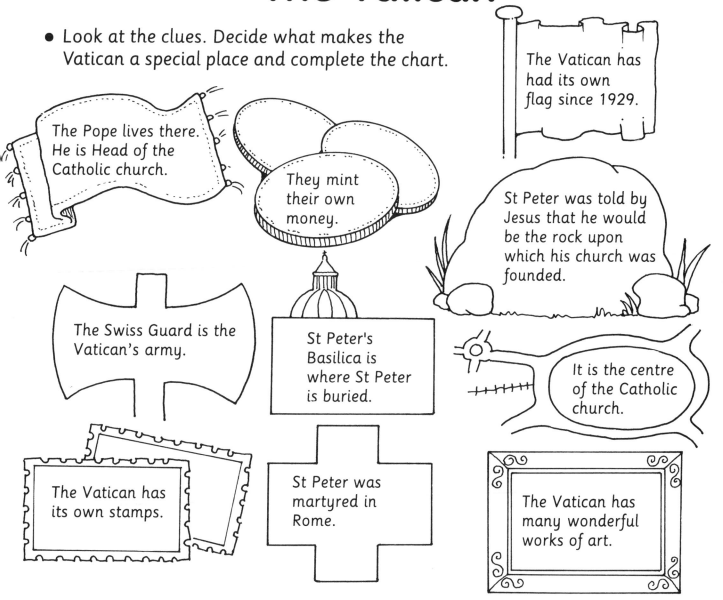

The Vatican has had its own flag since 1929.

The Pope lives there. He is Head of the Catholic church.

They mint their own money.

St Peter was told by Jesus that he would be the rock upon which his church was founded.

The Swiss Guard is the Vatican's army.

St Peter's Basilica is where St Peter is buried.

It is the centre of the Catholic church.

The Vatican has its own stamps.

St Peter was martyred in Rome.

The Vatican has many wonderful works of art.

Religious reasons	Other reasons

• Which of these reasons would make the Vatican special for Roman Catholics?

The Promised Land – Ideas Page

Aim

To tell the story of the Exodus and reveal Jewish and Christian views of God.

Activity Sheet

- The quest for a better place is a frequent theme in songs, such as *Somewhere over the Rainbow*. Form the children into pairs and ask what they would change, if they could, to make the rules for a better world.
- Use the activity sheet for recording the children's responses. Make a display of their responses.
- Another possibility is to ask the children to write a simple list poem: 'Heaven is... no more starving children, the warmth of the early afternoon sun and so on'.

Starting points

- Share with the children that the Exodus and the Promised Land are foundations in the Jewish faith. 'Therefore let us rejoice at the wonder of our deliverance... from darkness to light, from slavery to redemption. Before God let us sing a new song.' The 'Promised Land has come to mean a place where all is well and there is no disharmony.
- Tell the children the story of Moses and Joshua which can be found in Exodus, Numbers and Joshua in the Bible, or ask them to research it.
- Tell the children the story of the Ten Plagues.

Serpents Rivers of blood Frogs Flies

Cattle plague Boils Hail Locusts

The Ten Plagues

Darkness Death of first-born

Developments

- Look at the central issues of the Promised Land story:
  - **Slavery:** What must the life of a slave be like? Are there any advantages? What were slaves used for in Egypt?
  - **Excuses:** Moses tried to persuade God he was not the right man (Exodus 4). What sort of excuses do we make?
  - **The plagues:** Draw pictures of the ten plagues. Ask children to sequence them correctly.
  - **Promises, promises:** Discuss what making promises means. Is there a danger in making them? Have any children ever had a promise broken? What does the story say about God's faithfulness?
  - **Reliance on God:** In what ways did the Jews rely on God through the period of the Exodus and desert wanderings?
  - **Evidence of God's presence:** What evidence was there of this?
  - **How would you have felt?:** Try to see the story from different perspectives - the pharaoh, Moses, an ordinary person. How would each of them have felt?
  - **Leadership:** What sort of leader was Moses? List his qualities.
  - **The Ten Commandments:** Why do we need rules to live by? What rules do you think are necessary?

TEN COMMANDMENTS
1. You shall not commit murder.
2. You shall not steal.
3. You shall not give false evidence against your neighbour.
4. You shall not covet your neighbours home.

Rules for the world

- If you ruled the world, what would you change?
- Write your rules for a better place.

The road to Damascus – Ideas Page

Aim

To introduce children to the story of Paul's conversion in a variety of ways.

Activity Sheet

- Saul's conversion is often spoken of as coming out of darkness into light. Ask the children to sequence the pictures on the activity sheet. They could then compare their versions with the Bible story (Acts 8–9).

Starting points

- Ask the children to write down times when they have changed their mind about something important. Who or what changed their mind?
- Paul (Saul) felt very angry about Christians. What makes the children really angry? Why? What sort of things do people do when they are angry? They could carry out a survey and record their findings in a graph or a chart.

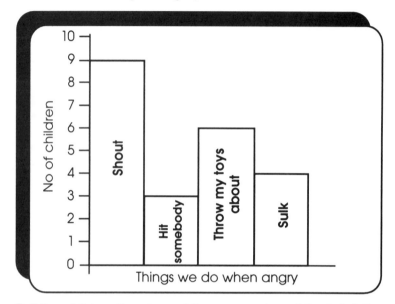

- Tell the children the story of the conversion of Saul. A full account can be found in Acts: 8–9.

Developments

- Talk about what Saul's feelings and thoughts might have been while watching Stephen's stoning, on his way to Damascus before, during and immediately after his experience. How would Ananias the priest have felt about visiting this fierce persecutor of Christians? How did the Jews of Damascus feel about Paul's transformation? Ask the children to imagine that they were Paul escaping from the city in a basket, and act it out.
- What sort of man was Saul before his conversion and after it? The children could divide a piece of paper into two halves and write down their ideas.
- Damascus was a very special place for Paul. The children could imagine they are Paul and write their account of events as if they were writing their diary. They should explain why Damascus will be forever an important place in their life.
- Paul's whole life is full of incident and drama. Read about his travels, accomplishments and adventures in Acts in the Bible, and produce newspaper headlines or articles on them. Why not interview Paul for a radio programme?

The road to Damascus

- Match the pictures to their labels.
- Put the pictures in order to tell the story of Saul.

Saul sees again when Ananias blesses him.	Saul is baptised a Christian. He becomes Paul and speaks the Christian message.
On the road to Damascus, Saul sees a bright light. Jesus asks him, 'Why do you persecute me?'. Saul is made blind.	God speaks to Ananias, the priest and tells him that Saul must become a disciple. Ananias visits him.
Saul wants to search for and persecute Christians in Damascus.	Saul, a Jew, hates Christians and is involved in the stoning of Stephen.

What a wonderful world! –

Aim

To learn about the aborigine's lifestyle and view of the world, and how they see their world as a very special place.

Starting points

- Talk about the aborigine's view of the world and introduce the idea of Dreamtime.
- Tell the children a made-up Dreamtime story of your own, based on the activity sheet. Create a special atmosphere, by sitting on the floor, darkening the room, and telling the story by candle-light.

Handed down from generation to generation have been many stories about the creation of the land (Dreamtime stories). Many tell of Baiame, the Maker of all things, who caused Dreamtime to begin. Dreamtime characters undergo epic journeys and adventures. As they travel, argue and solve problems so they cause the landscape to change shape. Aborigines believe that the land is special and sacred. They do not feel they own the land but rather that the land owns them.

Activity Sheet

- Give pairs of children an activity sheet and ask them to cut out and sequence the parts of the story.
- Groups of four children could compare their outcomes and discuss any differences.

The beginning of the world – correct order for the activity sheet

1. The Earth is barren and flat.
2. The Rainbow Serpent awakes.
3. The Rainbow Serpent gets lonely.
4. The frogs look funny and get tickled.
5. All the creatures have woken up.
6. Emu and Eagle have an argument.
7. Rainbow Serpent swallows misbehaving creatures.
8. Rainbow Serpent makes the laws.

How we can care for our world.

1. Re-use bottles and re-cycle paper etc.
2. Don't use CFC aerosols.
3. Don't make lots of rubbish.

Developments

- Most religions have beliefs on how the world was created. The children could research these and compare them.
- The psalmists of the Old Testament frequently burst into unrestrained joy and thankfulness to God at what they see as the beauty of the Earth. Psalm 98 says 'Sing to the Lord all the Earth; praise him with songs and shouts of joy!.... Roar, sea, and all creatures in you; sing Earth... ' Discuss the beauty of nature and the world around. What amazes and impresses the children? Try and capture thoughts in writing or compose prayers of thanks to God.
- Embedded in the aborigine's thinking is the responsibility of caring for their world and looking after it. Look together in a practical way at how you can make a difference to your school and immediate environment. Discussing issues of pollution, conservation and recycling could help. Look into the work of worldwide conservation groups, like the World Wide Fund for Nature.

The beginning of the world

- Read the story of the Australian Aborigine Dreamtime.
- Put it in the correct order.

 After a while it got lonely so the Rainbow Serpent decided to wake up the other creatures. The big-bellied frogs were the first to emerge. Their stomachs were full of water they had stored.

 In the beginning the Earth was barren and flat. Nothing grew. Nothing moved. It was dark. All the birds, animals and reptiles were asleep under the ground.

 The frogs looked so funny that the Rainbow Serpent tickled them with her tongue. They laughed so much that all the water inside them started to rush out. It filled the tracks and hollows left by the Rainbow Serpent. This is how the lakes, rivers and seas were first formed.

 One day the Rainbow Serpent woke up and began to look around. Wherever she crawled she left a winding track. Wherever she slept she left a huge hollow in the ground.

 After a while, Rainbow Serpent could stand it no longer. She called all the creatures together and gave them some laws to help them all live together in peace.

 Emu and Eagle had an argument. Eagle took one of Emu's eggs and threw it up into the sky where it burst into flames. And so the Sun came into being.

 After all the creatures had woken up and come out from under the ground, they all lived happily together. But then things started to go wrong and they began to argue and fight.

 On other occasions when creatures misbehaved themselves Rainbow Serpent would slither up and swallow them. She spat out their bones and made hills and mountains of them.

Heaven – Ideas Page

Aim

To consider the children's ideas of Heaven, and to learn something of the beliefs of other religions.

Material Paradise	How to better spend money
Big, fast cars.	Charity for poor and disadvantaged.
Fur coats - expensive clothes, diamond rings.	Homes for homeless.
Expensive restaurants.	Food for the starving. Healthcare for all.
Cosmetics.	Education.

Starting points

- Ask the children for their ideas about Paradise. Could Paradise exist where everybody always had what they wanted? What are the problems when life revolves around 'I', 'me', 'mine' and 'self'? Outline the Buddhist concept of Nirvana, achieved by the ending of personal desire.
- List examples of how grown-ups often try to build a material Paradise on Earth. Ask the children what grown-ups could do with the money they spend on self-gratification.
- Introduce the variety of ideas about heaven.

Christianity Most Christians believe that by faith in Jesus, they are forgiven their sins and that eternal life awaits them in heaven. Heaven is described as Paradise (Luke 23: 43), as Sanctuary (Luke 13: 9).

Judaism 'Most Jews believe in heaven on earth, with body and soul being kept together' (Isaiah 34: 1–17). They do not believe heaven is exclusive to Jews.

Islam 'They shall recline on jewelled couches face to face and there shall wait on them immortal youths with bowls and ewers and a cup of purest wine' (Surah 56: 4–42). Muslims believe that only those in heaven will see Allah (God).

Hindu A person's jiva (soul that is never born, never dies and is without gender) migrates from one body to another through reincarnation before it finally finds its atman (real self) and obtains moksha (release) from transmigration and achieves spiritual union with the Godhead, Brahman.

Sikhism Heaven is like the universe, vast and infinite, and each person's soul will become absorbed into God's being.

Buddhism Buddha said feelings, senses, powers of thought and physical features end at death. Only man's desire is reborn. Nirvana, or heaven, is a state of being.

Activity Sheet

- Outline and consider the spiritual qualities vital to all religions if believers are to aspire to heaven.
- Working in pairs or small groups ask the children to write them in order of priority on the 'Stairway to Heaven'. Compare results.

Developments

- Ask the children to write down arguments for and against the existence of Heaven.

Arguments for	Arguments against
Seeing is believing? Black holes cannot be seen, yet we are fairly sure they exist. Why not heaven? Seeds shrivel and die before they become beautiful plants. It follows that the human body, when it shrivels and dies, can be transformed into a new and glorious spiritual body.	Humans know they will eventually die, and need something to look forward to after death. One day even the sun and our solar system will die. Why should something exist afterwards?

- Ask them to draw or paint their own versions of Heaven and create a gallery of their images to compare and contrast.

IDEAS BANK – *Special Places*

Stairway to Heaven

- Put the qualities on the stairway in what you think is the best order.
- Talk about how and why yours is different from other people.

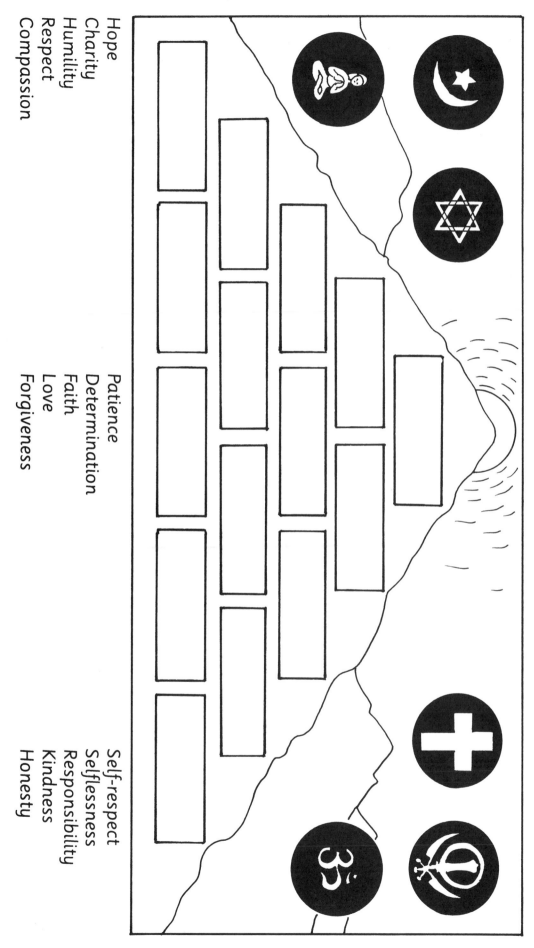

Hope
Charity
Humility
Respect
Compassion

Patience
Determination
Faith
Love
Forgiveness

Self-respect
Selflessness
Responsibility
Kindness
Honesty

8 ways to help ...

There are many ideas in this book about developing and extending the photocopiable pages. Here are just eight ways to help you make the most of the **Ideas Bank** series.

1
Paste copies of the pages on to card and laminate them. The children could use water-based pens that can be wiped off, allowing the pages to be re-used.

2
Put the pages inside clear plastic wallets. They could be stored in binders for easy reference. The children's writing can again be easily wiped away.

3
If possible, save the pages for re-use. Develop a simple filing system so that the pages can be easily located for future use.

4
Use both sides of the paper. The children could write or draw on the back of the sheet, or you could photocopy another useful activity on the back.

5
Make the most of group work. Children working in small groups could use one page to discuss between them.

6
Photocopy the pages on to clear film to make overhead transparencies. The ideas can then be used time and time again.

7
Use the activity pages as ideas pages for yourself. Discuss issues and ideas with the class and ask the children to produce artwork and writing.

8
Customise the pages by adding your own activities. Supplement the ideas and apply them to your children's needs.